# NARWHAL

## UNICORN OF THE SEA

# BEN CLANTON

SCHOLASTIC INC.

FOR ENYA
A.K.A. NUNU, A.K.A. JELLYFISH-FLINGER,
A.K.A. MERMICORN

ISBN 978-1-338-20041-6

24 23 22                                          19 20 21 22

Printed in the U.S.A.                          40

First Scholastic printing, May 2017

Edited by Tara Walker
Designed by Ben Clanton and Andrew Roberts
The artwork in this book was rendered in colored pencil and colored digitally.
The text was hand-lettered by Ben Clanton.
Photos: (waffle) © Tiger Images/Shutterstock; (strawberry) © Valentina Razumova/Shutterstock

# CONTENTS

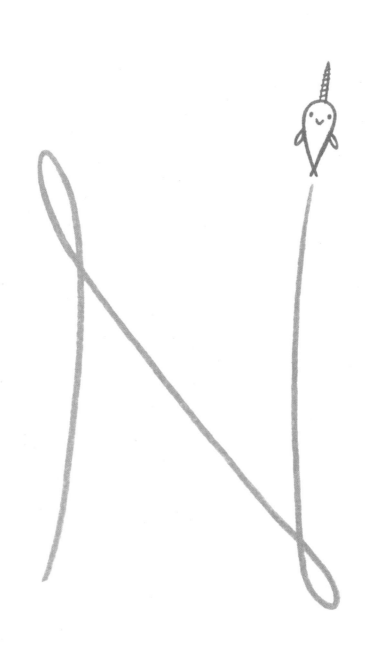

NARWHAL IS REAL ly AWESOME

ONE DAY WHEN NARWHAL WAS OUT FOR A SWIM, HE FOUND HIMSELF IN NEW WATERS.

ARE YOU REAL?

LAST TIME I CHECKED.

ARE YOU?

AM I WHAT?

REAL!

UM...YEAH, I'M A JELLYFISH.

JELLYFISH? heehee! THAT SOUNDS FUNNY!

I CAN'T BELIEVE THIS!
THE THING I'M IMAGINING
IS IMAGINING THAT IT
IS IMAGINING ME.

PROVE IT!

PROVE WHAT?

PROVE YOU'RE REAL!

CAN YOU PROVE THAT YOU ARE REAL?

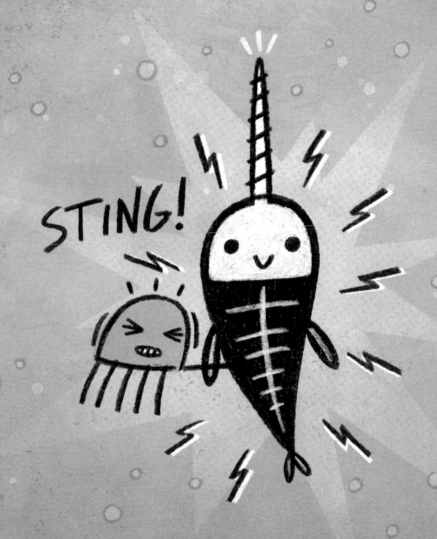

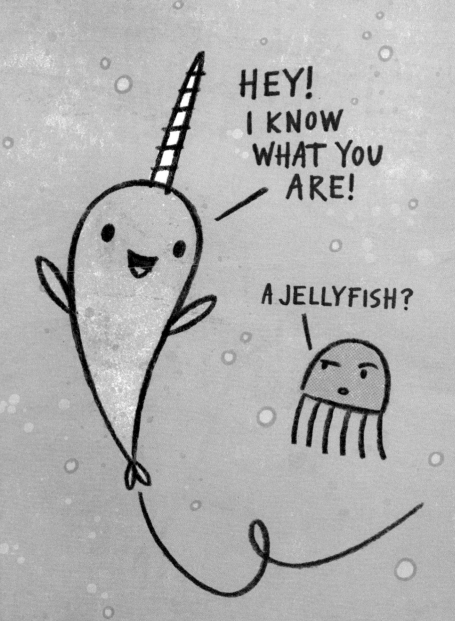

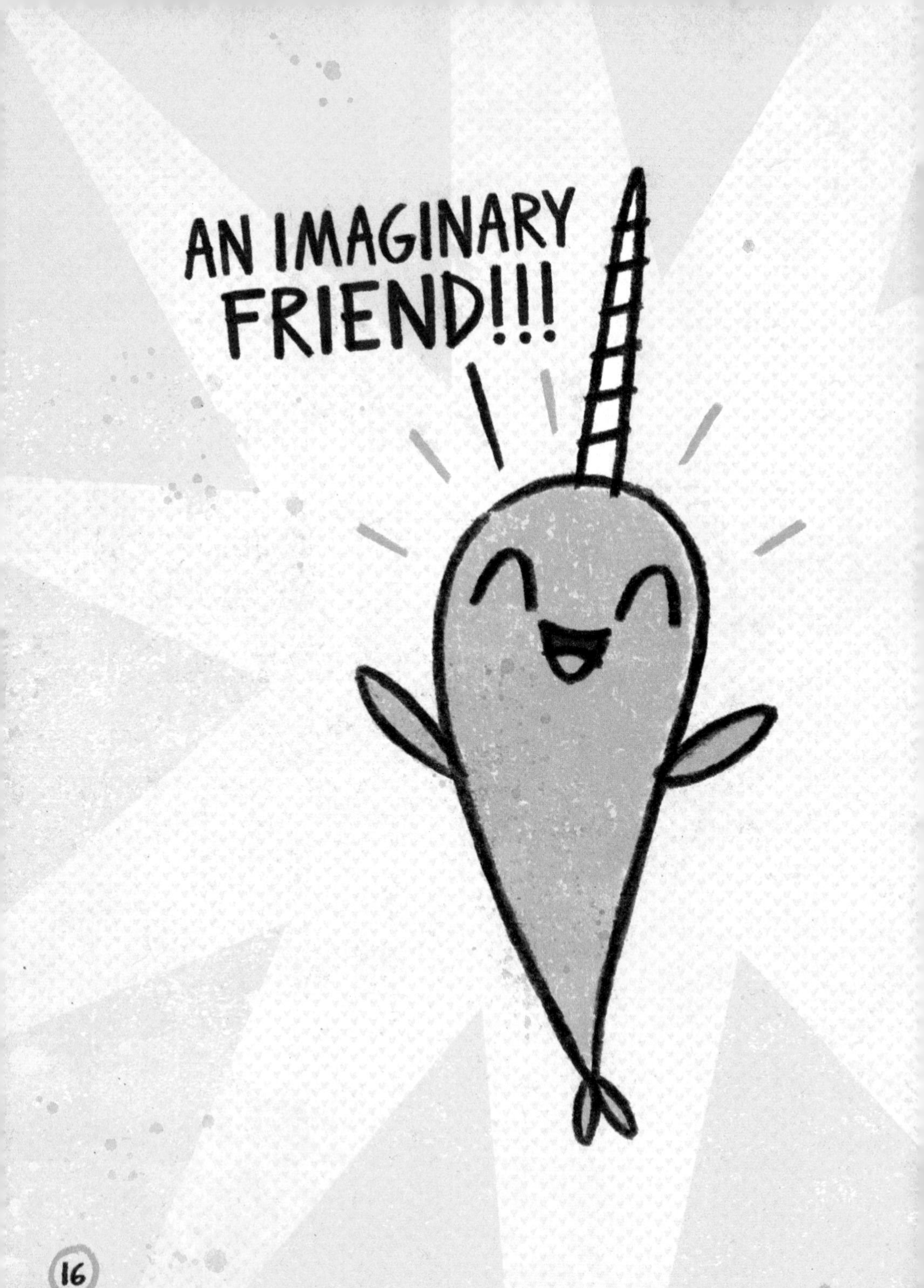
AN IMAGINARY FRIEND!!!

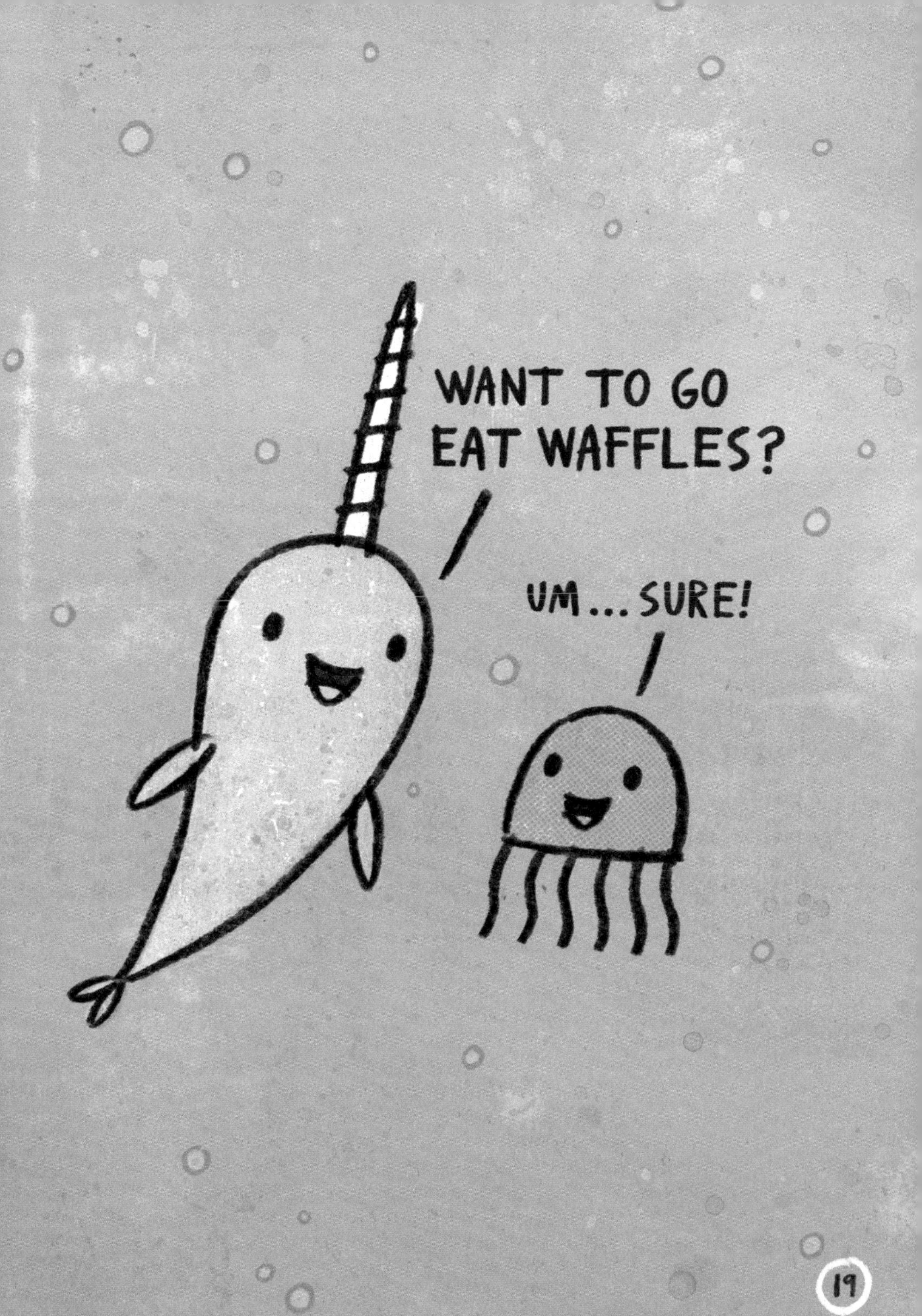
WANT TO GO EAT WAFFLES?
UM... SURE!

# REALLY FUN FACTS

A NARWHAL'S LONG, HORN-LIKE TOOTH CAN REACH UP TO 3 m (10 ft.) LONG!

I BRUSH EVERY DAY!

WOW!

I'M AMAZING!

NARWHALS CAN WEIGH 1,600 kg (3,500 lb.) AND HOLD THEIR BREATH FOR 25 min.

THE RECORD DIVE DEPTH FOR A NARWHAL IS 1,800 m (5,905 ft., OVER ONE MILE).

RECENT RESEARCH SUGGESTS NARWHALS CAN LIVE UP TO 90 YEARS.

# MORE REALLY FUN FACTS

THERE ARE NEARLY 4,000 TYPES OF JELLYFISH IN THE WORLD.

WHOA!!! I WONDER WHAT KIND I AM...

THE AWESOME KIND!

NOT TO BE CONFUSED WITH A SNACK.

A GROUP OF JELLYFISH IS CALLED A SMACK.

JELLYFISH HAVE BEEN AROUND FOR MILLIONS OF YEARS. WELL BEFORE DINOSAURS!

THE STING FROM SOME JELLYFISH CAN BE DEADLY FOR HUMANS.

THE DEADLY ONES ARE FOUND MAINLY IN AUSTRALIA.

# NARWHAL'S POD OF AWESOMENESS

25

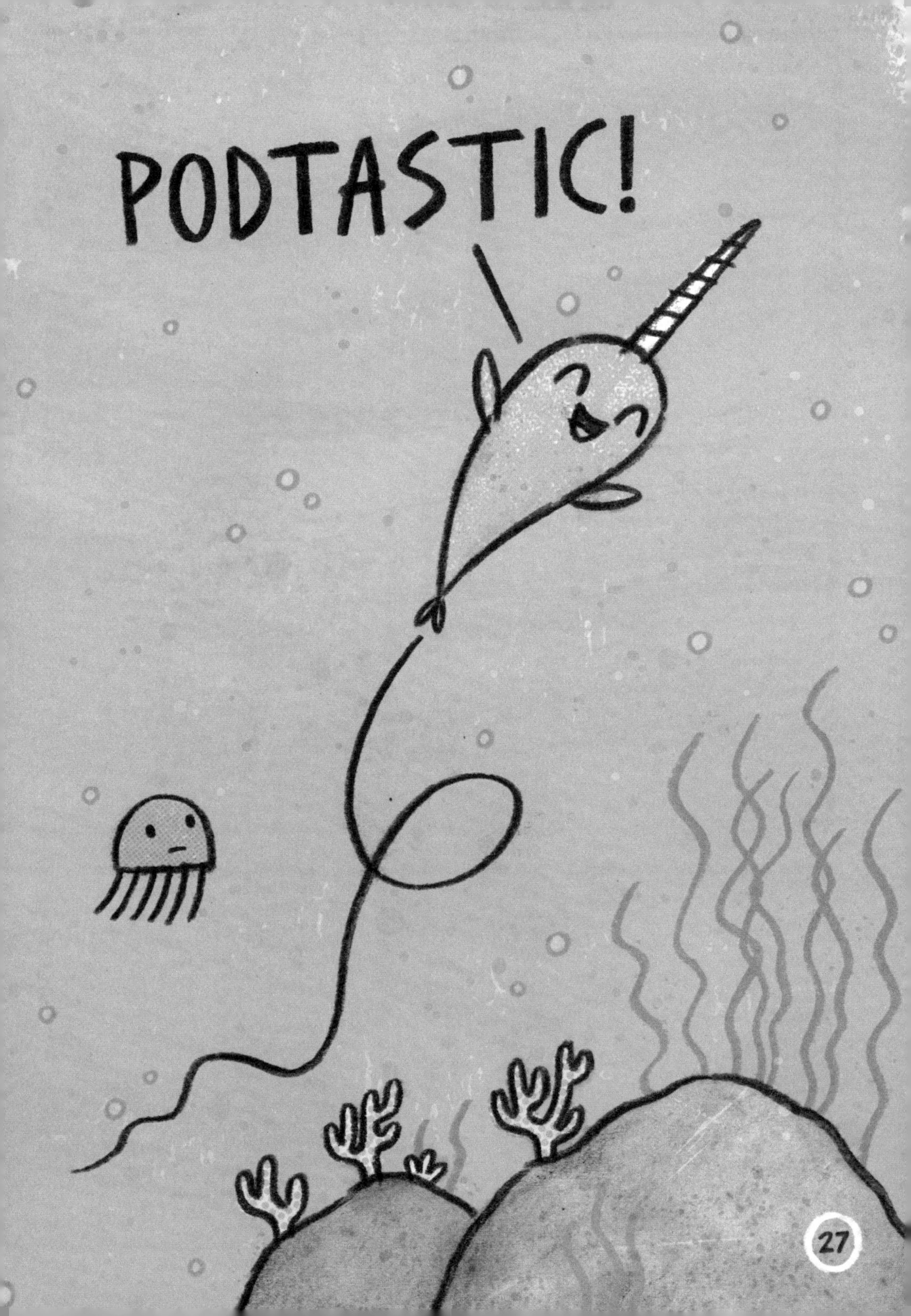
PODTASTIC!

OKAY.

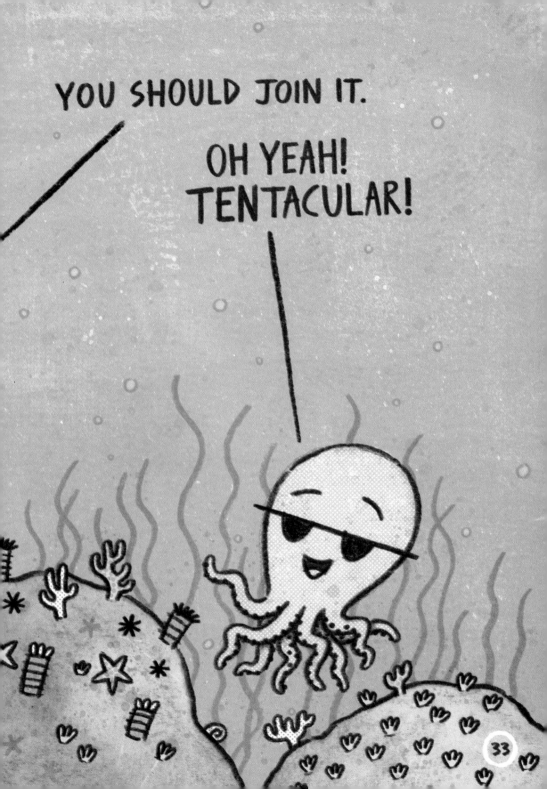

# NARWHAL!
## AREN'T YOU GOING TO ASK ME TO JOIN?!

# I'M NOT REALLY SURE!

BUT I IMAGINE A POD PLAYS
ULTIMATE CANNONBALL, EATS
WAFFLES, FIGHTS CRIME AND...

HAS SUPER AWESOME PARTIES!

I DO LOVE PARTIES!

# PODTASTIC!

NARWHAL!

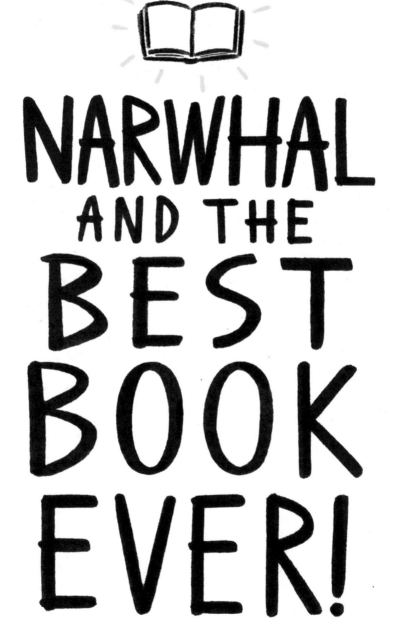

# NARWHAL
## AND THE
# BEST
# BOOK
# EVER!

WHAT ARE YOU READING?

MY FAVORITE BOOK IN THE WHOLE WIDE WATER AND PROBABLY THE REST OF THE UNIVERSE TOO!

WOW! CAN I SEE?

SURE THING!

UM...NARWHAL?

FLIP!
FLIP!

THIS BOOK IS...

FLIP.

BLANK.

IT'S AN IMAGINATION BOOK, JELLY! YOU'VE GOT TO PRETEND!

UM...OKAY...

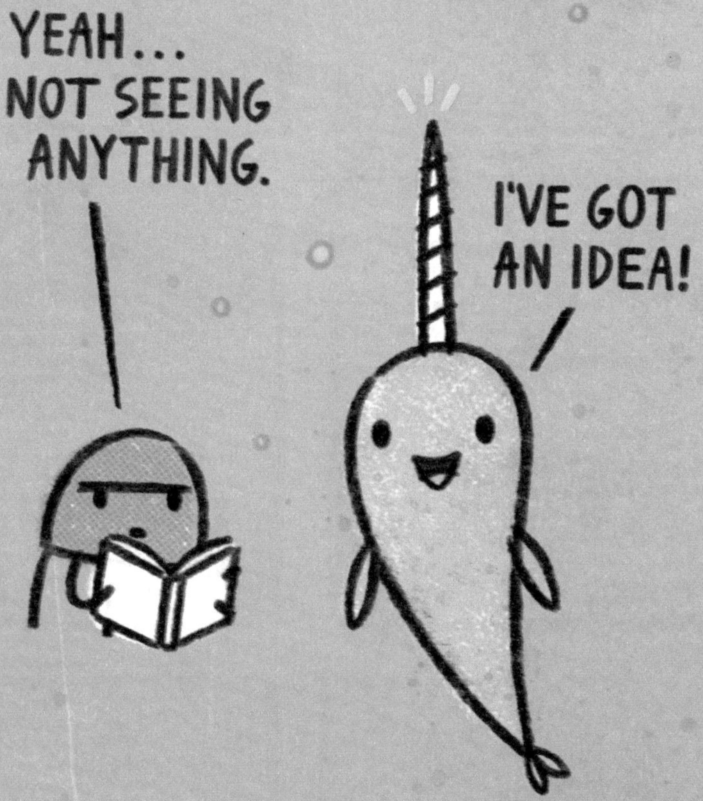
YEAH... NOT SEEING ANYTHING.
I'VE GOT AN IDEA!

FIRST CLOSE YOUR EYES.

NOW WHAT?

NOW THINK ABOUT ONE OF YOUR FAVORITEST THINGS IN THE WORLD.

MAKE A PICTURE OF IT IN YOUR HEAD.

NEXT THINK ABOUT A ROBOT. PICTURE A GIANT ANGRY ROBOT!

789

I'M SCARED OF GIANT ANGRY ROBOTS!

GOOD THING THAT WAFFLE
IS A KUNG FU MASTER!

LOOK AT THE BOOK AND SEE
A PICTURE OF IT BATTLING
THE ROBOT!

NICE ONE, JELLY!

I GET IT, NARWHAL!
THIS BOOK IS THE BEST!
IT CAN BE ABOUT ANYTHING
YOU WANT IT TO BE ABOUT!

TURN THE PAGE!
I WANT TO SEE
WHAT HAPPENS NEXT.

JUST DON'T GET
THE PAGES WET.